Miscarriage

A Book for Parents

By Joy and Marv Johnson, Robin Bock, Carol Dannen,
M'Lee Hasslinger, Peggy Jaegly, and Sylvia Smith

Special thanks to Peg Lorkovic, Mary Vondra and Janet Roberts

Design by Centering Resources

Copyright ©1983
Centering Corporation
All Rights Reserved
Revised 2020

Centering Corporation is a nonprofit bereavement resource center.
We provide grief support literature.

Additional copies may be ordered from:

orders@centeringcorp.com

Phone: 1-866-218-0101

Fax: 1-402-553-0507

CENTERING
AND
GRIEF DIGEST MAGAZINE
GRIEF RESOURCES

*This book is dedicated to all miscarried babies,
their parents who love them, and the caring people
who recognize the unique grief of this experience.*

A Note from Joy and Marv

My first miscarriage was the most devastating thing that had ever happened to me. I had always trusted my body, and suddenly I had absolutely no control.

Mom in Toledo

The shock and fear of miscarriage can be overwhelming. You have severe physical pain, and you realize there's nothing you can do. Your whole world is thrown off balance. You lose your pregnancy. You lose your baby. You lose your self-control and you even lose something of yourself.

When you have a miscarriage you have a very real and powerful grief. It may be one of your first encounters with death. It is certainly something you never forget.

As we have traveled through the country doing workshops, we have become convinced that the experience of miscarriage is one of this country's great unresolved griefs.

This book was given to you by someone who cares, and we hope it will be valuable to you as you begin to experience your own grief and the grief of others.

Joy and Marv Johnson
Founders, Centering Corporation

The Special Oneness

I'm alone. And just two days ago I was never alone. . . I had always had baby inside me.

Mom in Iowa

Most miscarriages happen fairly early in pregnancy, at a time when you feel you have a secret that makes you bigger and taller, and the whole world takes on a rosy glow. You know you're pregnant, your doctor knows, people close to you know, and you begin to order your life around your baby. You have a sense of destiny, a promise of the future, a feeling of responsibility. Your baby becomes a real person to you. Between yourself and your baby there is a special, unique oneness that will last throughout the pregnancy, and because of that oneness, whether you miscarry early in your pregnancy or later, you will have lost a part of yourself when the baby dies.

Feelings

Just because no child was born and just because I didn't feel the life of that baby doesn't mean I didn't love, lose or mourn its leaving! So many people seemed to think I didn't really lose anything. Well those people make my baby a non-person. It wasn't a paperweight or a rock in my uterus. It was MY BABY--someone--even if I never saw the color of hair or shape of the face-a baby was there, just the same.

Mom in Omaha

Miscarriage results in feelings that may be new and difficult for you. You may feel numb, helpless or isolated from others. You may become anxious or afraid. Several different feelings will be referred to throughout this book, and you will be encouraged to accept your own feelings as unique and a normal response to your miscarriage. Three common feelings after a miscarriage are sadness, anger and guilt.

Sadness

Whenever you lose someone or something precious to you, you're sad. Your grief seems to come in waves, strong, then subsiding, then coming again. Now is the time to recognize that your sadness is a natural feeling and that your tears honor both yourself and your baby. You may be afraid to cry because you think it will make other people uncomfortable or make them feel bad. Even if that is true, it's not your job right now to take care of everyone else. Now is the time to give yourself permission to cry, to ask for a hug whenever you need one, and to know that tears are a warming, soothing release. They come. Welcome them when they come.

Anger

I was so mad at God that I didn't speak to Him for a year.

Mom in Ohio

A miscarriage can provoke your anger. Feeling angry can be healthy and normal at this time. You may have some anger at your own body which seemed to suddenly pull a mean surprise. You may put your anger onto your partner or family just because they are there. You may be angry at a medical community that seemed to treat your miscarriage routinely, and you may be angry at God. When you feel angry, you might want to find someone who will listen while you share your feelings. Sharing anger is healing, and you may even discover a new perspective to your feelings when you put them into words.

I had lost my baby. I packed to go to the hospital with tears streaming down my face. At his office, my doctor had told me I could get pregnant again, but just to make sure I had understood him correctly, I asked him again. He answered angrily, 'I told you you could. These things just happen!'

Mom in Ohio

Guilt

Most of the time both Dads and Moms feel they are in some way to blame for the miscarriage. We are a people who are taught to be in control, to be responsible. When something goes wrong we are taught to re-examine what we could have done or should have done to change the outcome. We feel there "must have been something" we could have done.

Keep in mind that guilt can be unproductive if you spin your wheels in self-pity and self-punishment. Staying stuck in guilt also uses energy that you need for other things right now. Remember that everyone who has a miscarriage has some guilt at one time or another. A positive, constructive use of your guilt is to ask questions and find realities.

Why Me? Why Ours?

We are a people who believe in reason and logic, cause and effect. It seems there should always be a reason. It is important that you sit down with your doctors, nurses and medical people who can help you search for answers and ask them all the questions you have thought about. Remember, there is no such thing as a dumb question. If it's important enough to worry you, it's important enough to ask. Ask direct questions and ask for honest answers. Review what you did right in your pregnancy. Think about what you might want to do differently in any future one. Realize you have a right to know the answers to questions about causes even if the answer you find is that there was no known reason for your baby to die.

Making a list of your questions can help sort them out in your mind and make sure that you include everything you need answered. Insist on the time you need to go over your questions to your own satisfaction. There is space for you to write down your questions on page 21 of this booklet.

Your nurses and doctors may have information to give you. Maybe they can find articles for you to read and sometimes give you lists of possible causes. Listen to what they say, and ask them for the help you need in learning about miscarriages.

Reaching In and Reaching Out

I don't like to think of myself as weak and needy. I resent the fact that I can't bounce back to normal, that I can't cope with my loss alone.

Mom in Iowa

You may find yourself withdrawing from people, becoming quiet and depressed, going into your protective shell and licking your wounds awhile. Your arms may actually ache for your baby, and you can feel terribly alone. There are times when you need to reach into yourself and find a quiet retreat. Reaching in can allow your grief to surface and allow your body and emotions to become restored.

However, too much reaching in can invite some depression. When you are depressed more than you want to be, you may need to realize it is time to stop reaching in for awhile. Now is the time, as soon as you are able, to get involved in something that will literally "move you"... both physically and mentally. Eat healthy foods and exercise as much as you are safely able. Think through your thoughts about the miscarriage and talk them out with someone who will listen constructively.

I felt guilty. There was a multitude of things I had done and I wondered if I had brought it on.

Mom in Ohio

There are times when you need to reach out to other people for their understanding and support.

Tell people what you need. When you need to be held or hugged, let someone who cares about you know.

Talk about your experience and about your feelings. A feeling shared is a feeling diminished. Talking about your miscarriage and your grief can allow you to see how it has affected your life and may help you move through your toughest times more easily.

When you need to get out of the house and visit someone else, call a friend and share a cup of coffee or soda together. It's OK to make the first move.

Last Moments

It's amazing
that the rest of the world
just keeps going on.

How can that be
when our very life
has been so changed
in only a moment?

By Dorothy Ferguson, from her book,
Little Footprints, Centering Corporation

Men and Grief

My experience with the miscarriage has been less emotional and more of a learning experience. What I did learn was more about my wife and that it's time for a couple to come close and communicate their many feelings.

Dad in Ohio

If you are a Dad whose baby died through miscarriage, your grief is likely to have a different tone and intensity than your partner's. Your greatest concern is probably for your partner, her pain and physical safety, and the assurance that she is well.

Since the woman carries and gives birth to the child you have made together, you don't quite experience the same "oneness" and loss of self that your wife knows. Her sadness may frighten you and go on longer than you expected.

You may find yourself the chief supporter, caregiver and hugger while not many people are inquiring about how you feel or if YOU need holding and caring. Remember, you don't always have to be strong.

You may assume some kind of blame for the miscarriage and be concerned about making love again because you don't want to "put her through that again." All these feelings are normal and natural.

You, too, have experienced the death of your baby, your dreams of the future and a part of your self-image.

I looked at her on the way to the hospital and said, 'I've never seen you look so sad.' She said, 'I've never been through this before.' For just a minute I had a sense of being a failure.

Dad in Omaha

You will probably have all the feelings your wife has of sadness, guilt, depression and anger. You'll have questions and concerns just as your wife needs love and care and someone to listen, so do you. Share your feelings with each other, ask for what you need, and if possible, visit with another couple who have also had a miscarriage.

The Two of You

The miscarriage was a totally new experience for both of us, and at times we held each other more than we talked.

Mom in Omaha

Most people think that a crisis such as a miscarriage brings couples closer together. The opposite can be true, too.

You'll probably discover each of you grieves differently. In our culture, women are generally allowed more tears and talk than men. Men are taught to hide their feelings and to literally "work" out their grief on the job. Recently, as we have all come to recognize the importance of feelings, more and more men are able to share their tears and their emotions.

Sharing your feelings can be very important right now. Your spouse is not a mind reader and really doesn't always know how you feel.

Say what you need, and give as best you can when you are asked.

Honor each other's feelings and allow time to integrate this experience into your lives.

Keep on "dating," even now. Say what you like about each other. Remember together how you met and how you came to fall in love. If you had funny or playful times together, recall them and laugh about them all over again.

Sometimes intimacy after miscarriage causes some hesitation. It can bring back memories, feelings, fears and tears. If you consider your first loving as a kind of gentle stroking and caring you'll probably find it a warm, close, comforting experience.

We just lay in each other's arms and let our tears run together.

Mom in Omaha

Your Baby

The doctor has been putting whatever it was he scraped out of me in a stainless steel bowl. Suddenly a nurse was carrying the bowl out of the room. And here is where I felt my second great loss. There was nothing I could touch and see. I felt extreme sadness that I had nothing to show that I had been pregnant.

Mom in Ohio

If you miscarried late enough in your pregnancy you may be able to see, hold, and touch your baby. Holding the tiny body in a soft blanket has been very helpful to parents and will give you a chance to say "goodbye", even if you haven't had an opportunity to say "hello". You may choose to have a small service or burial for your baby and give your baby a name, even if you have not yet chosen the name you would use at birth.

Some people thought the thing we did each year was crazy, but for us it was just right. We had told our other children that a new baby was on the way and they shared our sadness and knew we hurt when the miscarriage happened. I miscarried twins, and each year on the date that should have been their birthday, we have two little cakes for dessert and remember the twins. One of our little boys said they should be angel food cakes . . .and they always are.

Mom in Des Moines

There are many ways to memorialize your baby. You may want to:

Plant a tree, rose bush or other symbol of life.

Engrave a wall plaque or symbol of your religion with the baby's name and date of miscarriage.

Wear a charm with special meaning on your bracelet or around your neck.

Contribute to a special cause for children.

Send a flower to someone special on the anniversary of your miscarriage.

Do something special yourselves on the miscarriage date.

Have your baby's birthstone set into a ring.

Write your baby's name and date of miscarriage in the front of this book and keep it in a special place.

Make a bouquet of small flowers, dry it and put it in a special frame with your baby's name.

Light a candle in honor of your baby.

Volunteer for a non-profit organization and help others who are in need.

Make a quilt square, or embroider a special pillow that you can hold in memory of your baby.

And remember, taking care of yourself is one of the best ways you can honor your baby right now.

Single Moms

If you're a single Mom, many people will think you'll be relieved by your miscarriage and that it's "for the best." This may or may not be true. Most women feel some mixed feelings when they're pregnant. . .both wanting to be pregnant and at the same time not being so sure about it. Being single, you may have had more than your share of mixed feelings and concern from the very beginning. Remember, your feelings are real and your sadness is deep.

You may have put a lot of dreams and plans into your baby, and now feel especially alone with your loss. It's important for you to share your feelings with someone who will listen without telling you how to feel and who will be available when you want to talk. Your hospital staff can help you meet people who will give you the support and caring you need right now. Your feelings are valuable, and now is the time to take care of yourself.

Other Children

If you have other children, they need special consideration. They need to be told honestly that the baby died, that they were not to blame, and that all of you can take part in remembering the baby. If you have a burial for your baby, older siblings can choose something of their own to place in the casket. If there is no burial, your children may want to plan a service of their own or make something to hang on the wall to honor the baby and your family's sadness. You can ask a friend to send the siblings a sympathy card just for them.

Answer their questions honestly, reassure them in many ways you love them, and that you appreciate the way they are loving you right now. Often children take care of their parents when the parents are sad, and knowing that you recognize their consideration can be important to them.

Relating to Others

If people have not had a miscarriage themselves or in their immediate family, they may not realize that it is a sad and important event. People are embarrassed and uneasy because they just don't know what to say. We've all been led to believe that there are some magic words to say that will automatically make the sad person feel better. Oftentimes you end up feeling worse.

The words that hurt me are things I may have said myself to friends who miscarried. I understand that people who say things that hurt do so without being aware, with all good and helpful intentions, and that at least they have come forward and given me time and attention and have not turned away.

Mom in Iowa

When we're grieving we're likely to be more sensitive to upsetting kinds of comments than we are to touches, tears and kind words.

When people say things you consider either inappropriate, stupid or hurtful, you may want to simply state how you feel and leave it at that without getting angry or defensive. It may help if you receive poorly worded statements as awkward gifts given in good faith.

There are also some things you can say if you sense people drawing away from you and being uneasy. These will let people know they don't have to be afraid or careful of you:

We had a miscarriage, our baby was only ___ months along, so she/ he/it couldn't live. We have named the baby ___ and it helps (doesn't help) to talk about it. **Or,** *We need you to be with us and love us and understand how miserable we feel.*

Making a list of all the really loving and supportive things that come your way in the next few months can be a positive reminder in times when you need good memories.

Your Future

We live in a time when more and more couples are carefully planning their families. To have a miscarriage may lead you to think your entire life program has been destroyed. You may be blinded by the disappointment you feel. Give yourself time to think about the choices you've made. Talk about the good times you have as a couple and what is really important to you. Talk about charting a continued life course together and visit with people you trust about the options you have in planning your tomorrows.

Your miscarriage was probably unexpected. It caught you by surprise. Not only was your future caught off balance, you probably also became vulnerable and afraid.

List Your Fears

If you decide to become pregnant again, you'll probably have a lot of questions and fears. You'll hear that if you miscarry a first pregnancy you may miscarry the second. You'll hear that each pregnancy is different and that your next one will be fine. Either way, you're likely to have some anxiety.

Putting your fears into a list lets you look at them one by one rather than feeling overwhelmed by them or having them lurk about in the shadows. You can talk about them more clearly and find out if your worries about future pregnancies and your own future are realistic. If they aren't, you'll feel relieved. If they are real, find out what you can do about the situation. You can list your fears on page 23 of this booklet.

Residuals and Reminders

Something that lasts and lasts and doesn't go away is a residual. There are lots of lasting things in a miscarriage that will cause your hurt to resurface time after time and remind you of your loss.

If I looked out the window I saw pregnant women or mothers with children. All the TV ads were for baby products.

Mom in Ohio

This list of things that may cause you to remember and hurt may help you be somewhat ready for them as they come:
• Seeing the hospital nursery, hearing babies cry.
• Leaving the hospital empty handed.
• Going home with empty arms.
• Seeing the nursery you had planned.
• Seeing babies, mothers, and women who are pregnant.
• Baby showers for friends, baby announcements.
• The baby food aisle in the grocery store.
• Standing behind someone buying diapers.
• Playgrounds, parks and maternity stores.
• Packing away your maternity clothes.
• Signs and posters for baby-sitters.
• Subscriptions to baby magazines.
• Free parenting products and baby supplies.
• Cemeteries, funeral homes, symbols of death.
• A mother nursing in public.
• Baby product commercials on TV.
• Radio announcements about prenatal classes.
• Certain music.
• Anniversaries of the miscarriage and the due date.
• Intercourse (the beginning of the feelings).
• Buying a baby congratulations card for a friend.
• Letters from people who didn't know about the miscarriage.
• Seeing babies. . .everywhere.

The Sharing Community

Even while you feel the sharp aloneness of grief, you'll suddenly find you are part of a sharing community of people who have had a similar experience.

Women who had miscarried came out of the woodwork when I went back to work. It was as if they were now comfortable talking about it. . . I was one of them . . . and I knew I felt much of what they had felt.

Mom in Omaha

There is no acceptable, open, ritualistic way to share and grieve a miscarriage. You move from being part of a pregnant community where some of your friends and most of your thoughts were pregnant, to a caring community of people who know what miscarriage means. While it is no consolation to know that miscarriage is very common, being able to share with others who have been through it can be extremely valuable. Ask your nurse, social worker, chaplain or doctor about groups for parents who have had a miscarriage or infant death. To see that you are not having crazy, abnormal thoughts and actions--just having your feelings affirmed and supported by people much like yourself--is worth the effort of going to the meeting.

I did everything right! I was going to make sure that if I miscarried this time there wasn't going to be a single thing to make me feel I had done it. I was excited as each day went by and I didn't miscarry. Each day I would wake up and wonder if this was the day I'd lose the baby. As I passed the two time frames when I had lost the other two pregnancies, I relaxed. When I reached six months, I really began to relax.

Mom in Toledo

Moving On

I believe that I have achieved growth and developed personally from having first gone to the heights of ecstasy and then to the depth through miscarriage. I survived! After all my miscarriages and all the successful births I've had I really appreciate my children and find I and indeed wiser, if not always wider.

Mom in Iowa

A miscarriage can be a sad, disappointing experience. Abraham Lincoln once said, "It is attitude, not circumstance that determine what our lives will be." You may be able to use your miscarriage to become more sensitive to others who are experiencing grief in any form, to recognize new values and feelings such as a new appreciation for children and for life itself.

You may use your miscarriage to recognize that you have endured grief and despair and survived it with a new dignity and self respect. You may have found new ways to share your feelings with your spouse and people who are close to you. Maybe you learned that you could allow people to reach out to you and that you could ask for what you needed. And perhaps you are even surprised at your new maturity and wisdom.

We hope this book serves as a beginning.

Little Footprints

How very softly
you tiptoed into my world.

Almost silently,
only a moment you stayed.

But what an imprint
your footprints have left
upon my heart.

By Dorothy Ferguson, from her book,
Little Footprints, Centering Corporation

Special Terms

Below are words you may hear and which may cause some confusion and create questions for you. We give them to you as a quick reference. You may want to write down terms of your own to ask about when you are with your doctors or nurses.

Miscarriage: The word most often used by the general public to describe the very early delivery or loss of a baby when the mother is still in the earlier or middle stages of pregnancy.

Spontaneous Abortion: The medical term for miscarriage.

Missed Abortion: When your baby dies inside of you and it stays in your uterus for at least two weeks before your miscarriage occurs.

Incomplete Abortion: The baby leaves the uterus, but the placenta or life-support system for the baby stays inside.

Threatened Abortion: You have all the signs of miscarriage. Requires rest or hospitalization.

I.U.F.D: Stands for Inter-Uterine Fetal Death meaning the baby died in the uterus when you're near full term.

D and C: Dilation and Curettage, words that mean stretching your cervix or opening of your uterus and then scraping or using suction to very gently cleanse it of all the remains of the pregnancy.

Ectopic Pregnancy: The baby begins to grow outside your uterus, usually in the tube, and cannot live.

Questions and Answers

Making a list of your questions can help sort them out in your mind and make sure that you get everything you need answered. Write down your questions, concerns and answers here.

*The following letter is from the book, **Dear Parents**.. It is written by Martha Eise who is a counselor and coordinator of A. M. E. N. D. (Aiding Mothers and Fathers Experiencing Neonatal Death). She is the mother of two babies who died.*

Dear Parents,

I wish I could be with you right now, sharing a cup of coffee or tea. Since this is not possible, I will try to help you the best I can through this letter. I am so sorry to hear of the death of your baby. I can assure you I know what you are feeling. I have been there myself.

You are probably feeling very sad, maybe even angry. You might be feeling that no one really cares or understands how you feel. I can only assure you that you will not always feel as bad as you do now. I want to also tell you that you will never forget your baby, nor will you want to forget. That baby was a very special part of you and you will find yourself wondering, as the years go by, just what that child would look like or be doing. I know, because I do.

You are probably receiving some well-meaning advice from friends and family. "You are young, you can have other children. You can be glad the baby did not live, it would have been harder to lose it later. You have an angel in heaven." I know that none of these things are what you want to hear. Try to remember that people are only trying to make you feel better.

Another thought--please do not put a timetable on your grieving. Give yourself all the time you need. You will find that some days you notice you are feeling better and then you will have some bad days. That's all right, just give yourself time.

I hope this letter will be of some help to you. Please believe me when I say I know how and what you are feeling and I care.

Love and Concern,

Thoughts About Our Baby

You can use this space to make your own dedication or, write down other feelings, fears or events that are significant.

Other Supportive Resources

Miscarriage: A Man's Book
A note from Rick: Both of you face a lot of confusion and pain. You need to prepare for it. Your wife has some tough days ahead of her that you may not understand. As her husband, you'll share her struggles. However, sharing her pain won't be easy. You have your own pain to bear as you grieve the loss of this baby. Rick talks to men about difficult things, anger and grief.

Healing Together
For Couples Grieving the Death of Their Baby. This compact book covers ideas from the memorial service to talking together, information on how men and women grieve differently, and how to strengthen your relationship after the loss of your baby.

For Bereaved Grandparents
Grief is the normal reaction to a loss. Actually, we experience grief throughout our lives. A pet dies. A friend moves away. Our children go off to college. We lose a job. We grieve these losses, but we don't always realize that's what we are doing. With a grandchild's death, we face one of life's most painful griefs.

No New Baby-For siblings who have a brother or sister die before birth. Grandma took hold of my hand. She leaned over and picked something up off the ground. 'See this little bud?' she asked. 'It was supposed to keep growing and turn into a flower. But it didn't, and no one knows why. Most little buds become flowers, but some don't. This one died. It will never be a flower now.' I held the little bud in my hand. 'Just like our baby,' I said. Grandma explains you're not to blame and we don't always have answers.

Grief resources available at **centering.org.**